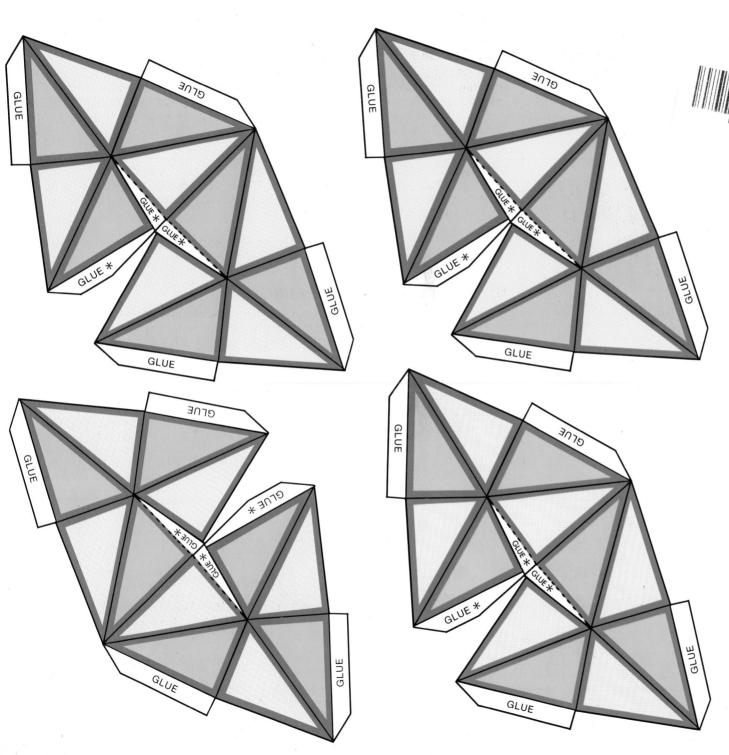

1. The Geodesic Sphere

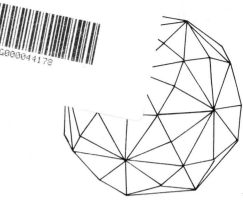

The shortest line between two points on a surface is called a 'geodesic line'. This delightful and curious model shows how 15 great circles — geodesic lines — can be found to form a complete symmetrical arrangement, dividing the sphere into 120 equal triangles.

HOW TO MAKE THIS MODEL

1. Cut out all the pieces on this page and on page 5, keeping well away from the outline.
2. Score along all fold lines.
3. Cut out precisely.
4. Fold and crease firmly. At every fold line fold away from you.
5. On each section glue the three flaps marked GLUE* first.
6. Glue the sections together to complete the model. Note that TEN triangles meet at each vertex where the sections meet. Leave section Y till last, and then close the final space with section Z.

For more information about geodesic spheres see page 2 of the minibook.

3

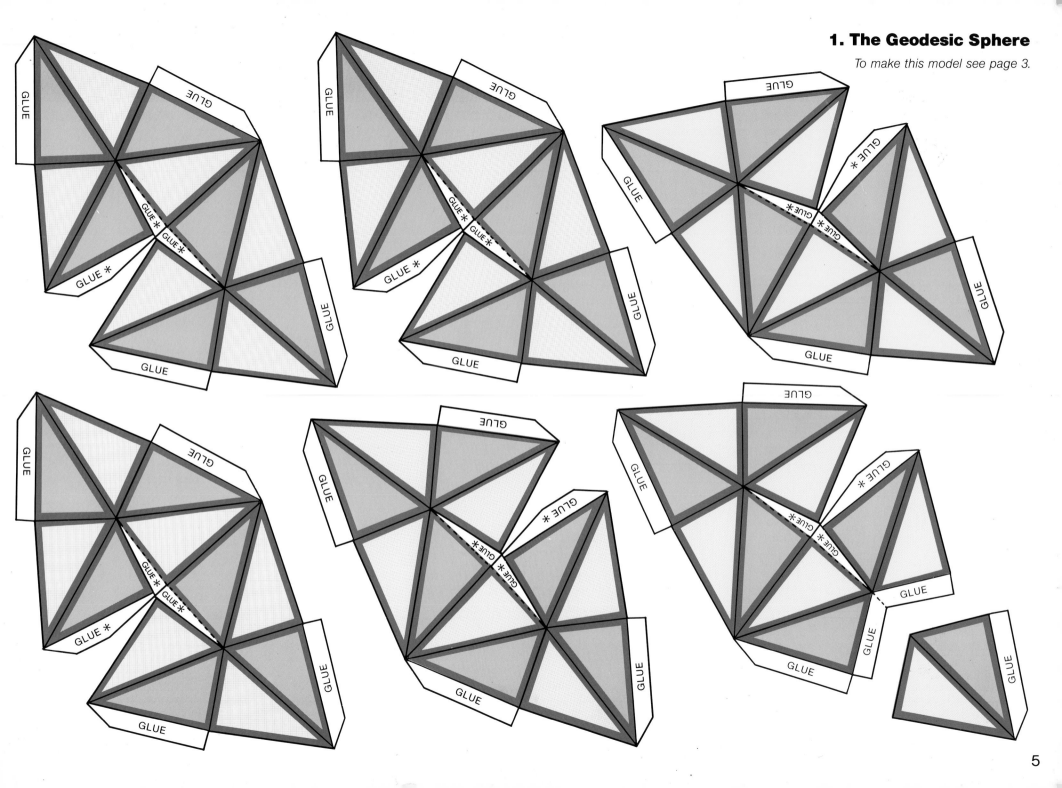

Section Y
GLUE LAST

Section Z
GLUE LAST

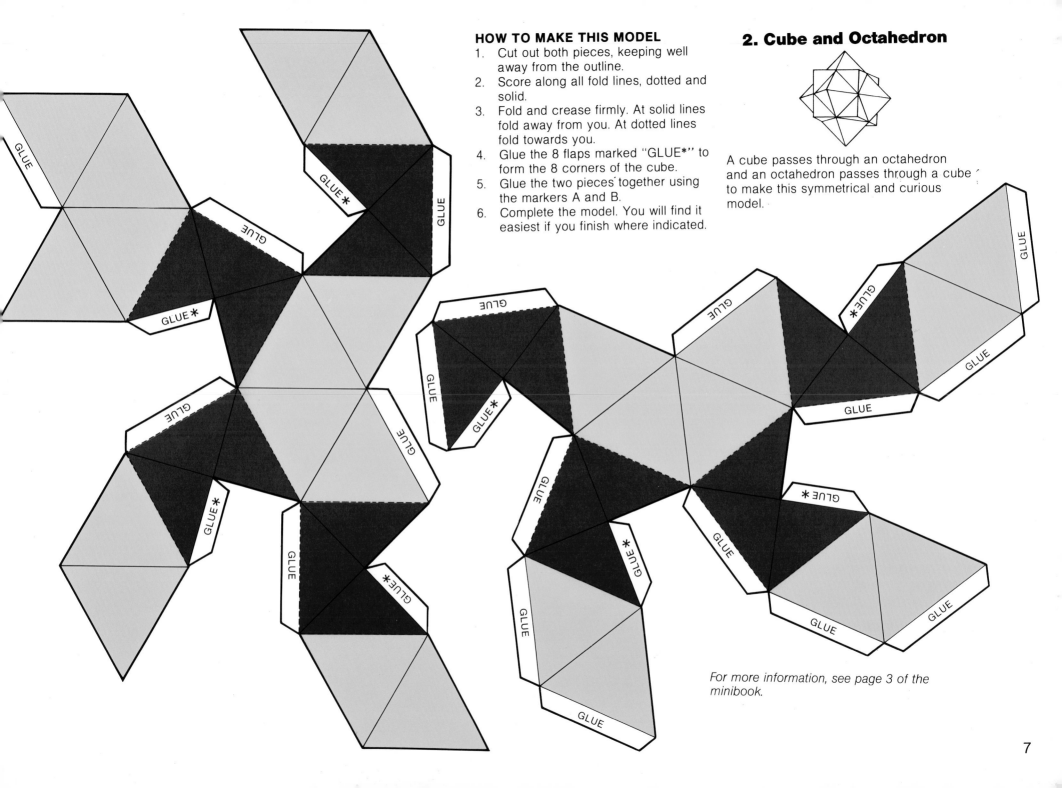

HOW TO MAKE THIS MODEL

1. Cut out both pieces, keeping well away from the outline.
2. Score along all fold lines, dotted and solid.
3. Fold and crease firmly. At solid lines fold away from you. At dotted lines fold towards you.
4. Glue the 8 flaps marked "GLUE*" to form the 8 corners of the cube.
5. Glue the two pieces together using the markers A and B.
6. Complete the model. You will find it easiest if you finish where indicated.

2. Cube and Octahedron

A cube passes through an octahedron and an octahedron passes through a cube to make this symmetrical and curious model.

For more information, see page 3 of the minibook.

A

B

A

B

GLUE
LAST

GLUE
LAST

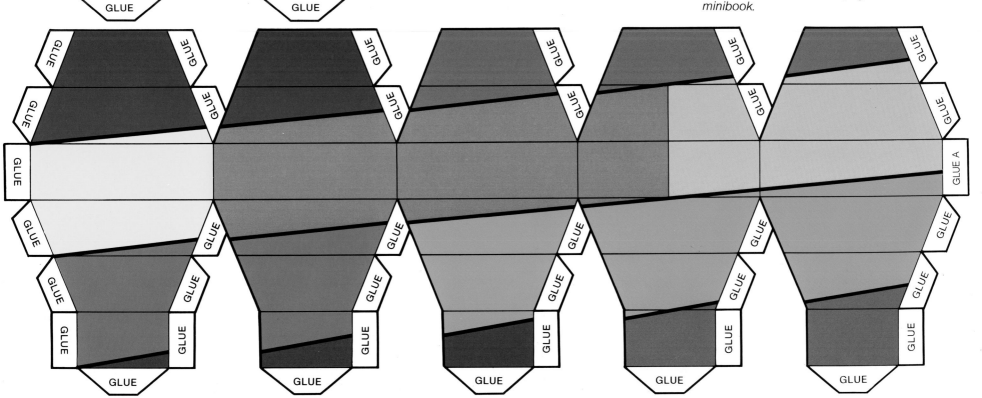

HOW TO MAKE THIS MODEL

1. Cut out both pieces, keeping well away from the outline.
2. Score along all fold lines, but **not** the thick spiral lines.
3. Cut out precisely.
4. Fold away from you along each fold line and crease firmly.
5. Join the two pieces together using the flap marked 'A'.
6. Complete the model. You will find it easiest if you start and finish where indicated.

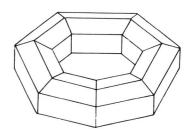

This model shows a curious property which is peculiar to a torus — or doughnut shape. It has been coloured with seven colours in such a way that each touches the other six.

On a plane or sphere, you will find that it is easy to arrange four colours so that each touches the other three, but no-one has been able to add a fifth or sixth colour, let alone a seventh — so this is a very remarkable model.

For more information see pages 4 and 5 of the minibook.

9

GLUE

LAST

A

GLUE FIRST

GLUE FIRST

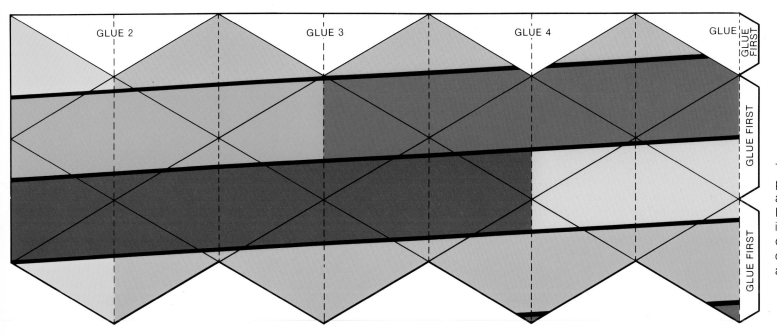

GLUE 2 · GLUE 3 · GLUE 4 · GLUE · GLUE FIRST · GLUE FIRST · GLUE FIRST

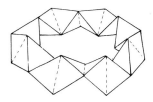

This model has the same seven colour property as the previous model, but moves as well!

For the seven sided torus is transformed into a ring of 14 linked tetrahedra which can be rotated for ever through their centre. Also, all the colours are of equal area and can be seen equally easily.

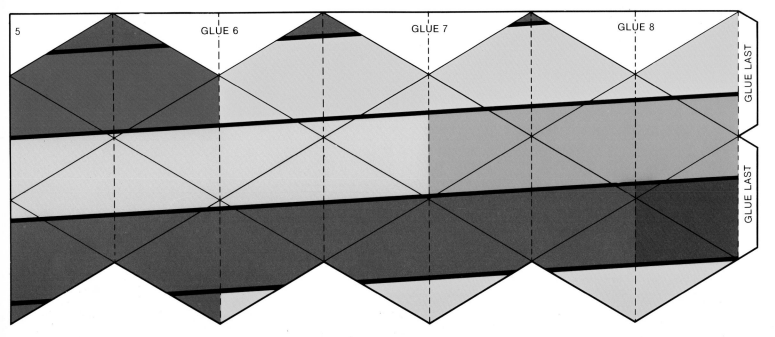

5 · GLUE 6 · GLUE 7 · GLUE 8 · GLUE LAST · GLUE LAST

HOW TO MAKE THIS MODEL

1. Cut out both pieces keeping well away from the outline.
2. Score along all the fold lines, both dotted and solid, but **not** along the thick spiral line.
3. Cut out precisely.
4. Fold and crease firmly. At solid lines fold away from you. At dotted lines fold towards you.
5. Glue the two pieces together using the three flaps marked "glue first".
6. When you can see how it goes together glue flaps 2, 3, 4, 5, 6, 7, 8 in order.
7. Complete the ring by glueing the two flaps marked "glue last". They go inside.

For more information, see page 5 of the minibook.

11

GLUE   GLUE 4   GLUE 3   GLUE 2

GLUE 8   GLUE 7   GLUE 6   5

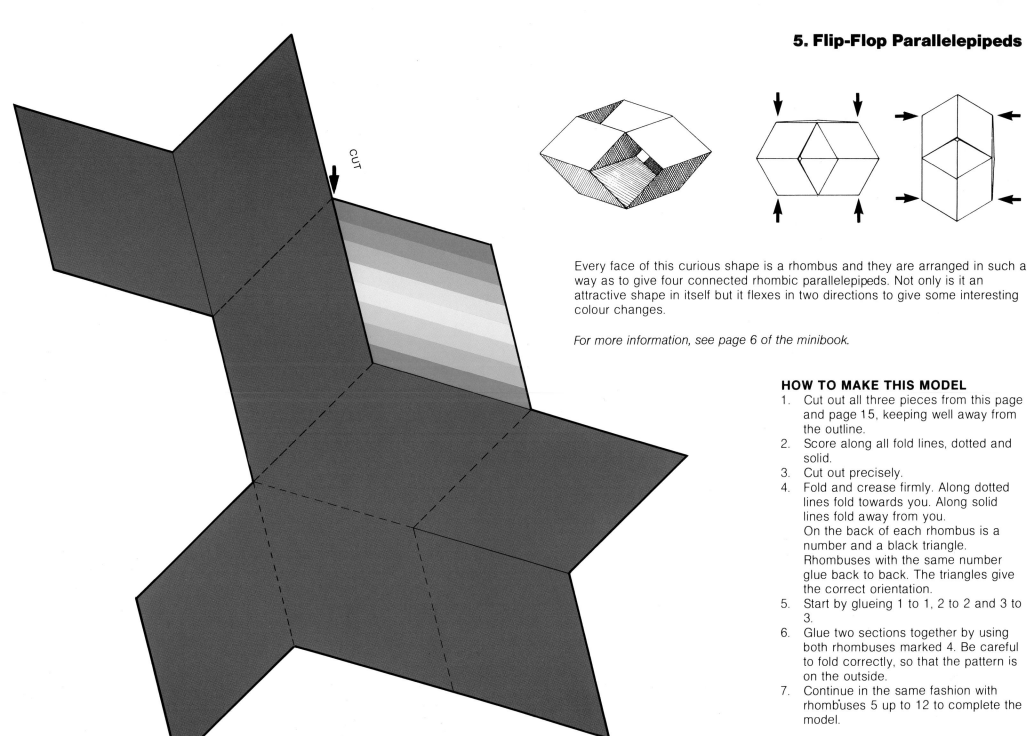

CUT

Every face of this curious shape is a rhombus and they are arranged in such a way as to give four connected rhombic parallelepipeds. Not only is it an attractive shape in itself but it flexes in two directions to give some interesting colour changes.

For more information, see page 6 of the minibook.

HOW TO MAKE THIS MODEL

1. Cut out all three pieces from this page and page 15, keeping well away from the outline.
2. Score along all fold lines, dotted and solid.
3. Cut out precisely.
4. Fold and crease firmly. Along dotted lines fold towards you. Along solid lines fold away from you.
   On the back of each rhombus is a number and a black triangle. Rhombuses with the same number glue back to back. The triangles give the correct orientation.
5. Start by glueing 1 to 1, 2 to 2 and 3 to 3.
6. Glue two sections together by using both rhombuses marked 4. Be careful to fold correctly, so that the pattern is on the outside.
7. Continue in the same fashion with rhombuses 5 up to 12 to complete the model.

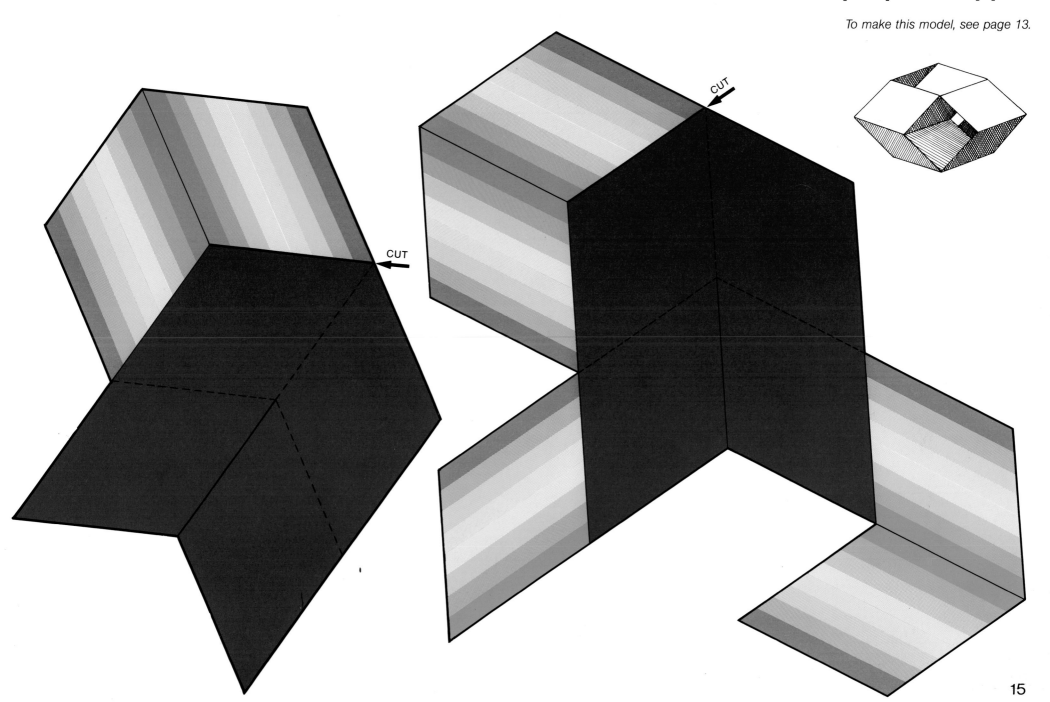

CUT

CUT

Mathematical
Curiosities 3

Some Curious
Mathematical Ideas

Suggested by this collection of models

Book 3

**Tarquin
Publications**

0 906212 25 1

Gerald Jenkins   Anne Wild

See inside the front cover for instructions on how to make the minibook.

Curious models . . .

1. The Geodesic Sphere
2. Cube and Octahedron
3. Seven Colour Torus
4. Seven Colour Rotating Ring
5. Flip-Flop Parallelepipeds
6. A Triangular Dissection
7. Pentagon and Pyramid
8. Pop-up Parallel Pyramids
9. The Flexitube Puzzle.

If you have enjoyed making these models, then there are other Tarquin books which may interest you. In particular, there are two more books in this series. At present there are three different series of books of mathematical shapes to cut out and make.

Make Shapes Series   **Books 1, 2, 3**
Mathematical Curiosities Series **Books 1, 2, 3**
Tarquin Polyhedra Series   **Books 1, 2, 3**

Tarquin books are available from Bookshops, Toy Shops, Art/Craft Shops and in case of difficulty directly by post from the publishers.

For an up-to-date catalogue, please write to Tarquin Publications, Stradbroke, Diss, Norfolk. IP21 5JP, England.

8. Pop-up Parallel Pyramids

Most pop-ups can be found as illustrations in books for young children, but there are further possibilities, mathematical subjects make good pop-ups too.

You might like to make a pop-up cuboid, which looks more solid than it really is. The net is given here.

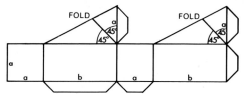 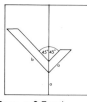

FOLD   FOLD

If you make the base the same size as the pop-up pyramids (8.5cm. x 9.7cm) then values of a = 2.5cm, b = 5cm give a good sized cuboid.

9. The Flexitube Puzzle

To turn the flexitube inside-out is not easy as you have no doubt found out! If your move doesn't give the pattern you want, look on the other side. When you can do it, it is easy!

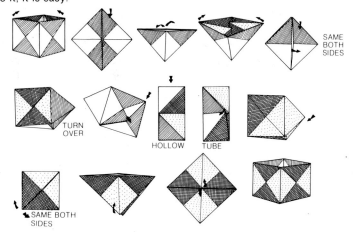

SAME BOTH SIDES

TURN OVER

HOLLOW   TUBE

SAME BOTH SIDES

8

1   2   3

4   5   6

7   8   9

Curious Mathematical Ideas . . .

1

1. The Geodesic Sphere

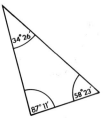

All 120 triangles have their angles as are given here, but you notice that 60 are like this and 60 are mirror images. This has been shown up by the colouring. The mathematical word for shapes which are mirror images of each other is that they are enantiomorphous.

If you would like to make another larger geodesic sphere for yourself, then it is easier to make 10 sets of 12 triangles, not 120 separate ones. The net is given here.

The architect R. Buckmaster Fuller is well known for his work on geodesic domes, which are developed from shapes like this model. Not only are the buildings beautiful and unusual, but they can be made to span large areas without support for Sports Halls and Exhibition Centres. They can also be made of lighter and thinner materials than conventional buildings.

A Rose By Any Other Name . . .

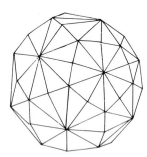

We hope that while you were making your model of the geodesic sphere, that you forgave us for choosing a name which was doubly wrong — firstly it was not a sphere and secondly the lines were not true geodesics!

Of course, it is impossible to make a sphere out of flat paper, but it is a good approximation and it does meet the sphere in no fewer than 62 points.

A geodesic is strictly the shortest line **on** the surface, not cutting through it as on the the model, but the visual impression is very similar. We also confess that the 'great circles' are not circles at all, but are polygons which approximate to a great circle.

However, we do think that the poetic licence is justified because it does make a very nice model, and it shows how 15 great circles can be arranged round a sphere in a completely symmetrical fashion.

7. Pentagon and Pyramid

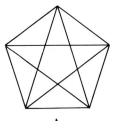

Of all the regular polygons, only the pentagon has the same number of diagonals as sides. It has five of each.

A pentagon also has the property that the diagonals form a smaller pentagon inside. The diagonals of the smaller pentagon form a still smaller one, just like the fleas in the immortal lines.

Big fleas have little fleas upon their backs to bite 'em and little fleas have smaller fleas – and so on, ad infinitum.

The diagonals of a pentagon on their own are called a pentagram, and this symbol has been used through the ages as a sign of black magic.

And as our model shows it is also a symbol of colourful magic!

Hexagons and Hexagrams

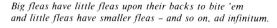

A regular hexagon also has many interesting properties. It has nine diagonals, but if you ignore the three which pass through the centre, the other six form a hexagram in a rather similar manner to the pentagram. If however you thought of using this hexagram as a basis for a folding pyramid, you would be rather surprised. Can you see why?

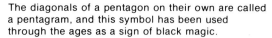

To make a folding pyramid with a hexagonal base of side a

You need a hexagon of side a, with isosceles triangles of side 2a on each side

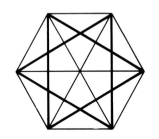

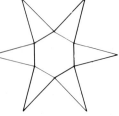

and you need six of these.

5. Flip-flop Parallelepipeds

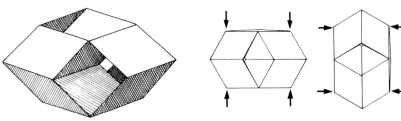

Each face of this shape is a 60° rhombus, and the 12 faces are joined together in a curious way so as to make four connected parallelepipeds which will flip into two different positions, both flat.

Since it is hollow, each side of every face can be seen, so there is nowhere for any hidden flaps. The puzzle then is to find a net so that 24 rhombuses glue together in pairs back to back and no extra flaps are needed. We found it an intriguing and difficult puzzle to solve. Can you do it?

Once you have solved the net, experiment with rhombuses with different angles — say 30° and 150° or 45° and 135°. Do they flip just as well, and can you find any other interesting properties?

6. A Triangular Dissection

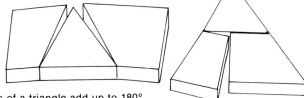

This model shows three things at the same time

1. That the angles of a triangle add up to 180°
2. That the area of a triangle is the same as the area of a rectangle with the same base and half the height.
3. That a model which dissects can be used as a base for interesting and unusual drawings and patterns.

If you would like to experiment with other drawings and designs which dissect, then we suggest that you use regular polygons divided in a regular way.

Experiment first on flat card, and then made a model when you have come up with something which works well.

6

2. Cube and Octahedron

This model is doubly pleasing. Not only do the two inter-penetrating solids show up clearly, but the completed shape is highly symmetrical. This is because the cube and the octahedron are what is known as **dual** figures. That means that each has the same number of faces as the other has vertices.

The cube has 8 vertices and 6 faces, and the octahedron has 6 vertices and 8 faces. If you look at your model you will see that each vertex of the octahedron is on the face of the cube and vice versa. It is this duality which makes the shape so attractive. Both have 12 edges.

There is a relation first stated by Euler which says

no. of faces + no. of vertices — no. of edges = 2

You will see that this is true for the cube, the octahedron and their combination. Try it on other shapes you can make.

At one time Euler's relation was thought to be true for all solids, but there are exceptions like the great dodecahedron and the small stellated dodecahedron.

Other Dual Combinations

A tetrahedron is self-dual because it has four faces and four vertices. The solid obtained by interpenetration is called the Stella Octangula.

A dodecahedron has 12 faces and 20 vertices, whereas an icosahedron has 20 faces and 12 vertices, so they are dual and make an interesting combination.

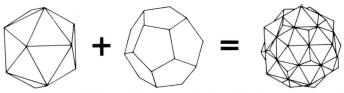

Neither of these models is too dificult to work out and make yourself — or the nets can be found in the book "Mathematical Models" by Cundy and Rollett.

3

See inside the front cover for instructions on how to make the minibook.

3. Seven Colour Torus

On a flat surface it is easy to draw three regions of colour where each colour touches the other two, or four regions where each touches the other three.

Simple as these problems are, no-one has been able to go further and find a diagram with five regions of colour each of which touches the other four.

It makes an interesting investigation to see if you can find a diagram for five colours. Does it make it easier if you work on the surface of a sphere or a cube?

You may recognise this as being a similar situation to the "four colour map problem", discussed in many mathematics books.

A Torus

This shape is sometimes called a 'doughnut', an 'anchor ring' or a 'quoit', but its mathematical name is a torus.

It is a curious fact that if the same five colour problem set out above is tried on a torus, then it is very easy to solve. The best way to work on torus problems is to look at a rectangle and then to imagine it being folded round and joined up at the ends and edges.

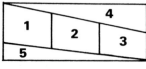
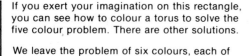

If you exert your imagination on this rectangle, you can see how to colour a torus to solve the five colour problem. There are other solutions.

We leave the problem of six colours, each of which touches the other five to you!

The solution for seven colours is more difficult and needs a spiral which goes three times round the torus before joining up. Try to work out how the colours are arranged. The model will help.

Making a Torus

A torus with curved surfaces cannot be made with paper, but it is possible to make interesting shapes which are simple topological transformations like your model.

If you would like to make another torus which has a hexagonal cross-section, then the net is given here. The first model has 7 sides in sympathy with the 7 colours and the angle x was 67° 22'.

If you would like to make one with six sides to colour with your solution, then the value of x is 63° 26'.

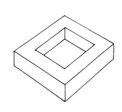 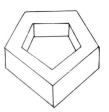

A Torus with four or five sides is possible too, and the cross-section doesn't have to be a hexagon.

4. Seven Colour Rotating Ring

Rotating rings are always good to make, however they are coloured. The net given below is for 7 tetrahedra, and two pieces make a 14 tetrahedra ring like your model.

You might like to make a 12-ring to illustrate your solution of the six colour problem or a 10-ring to illustrate the 5 colour problem. Any number larger than 7 will rotate, and any number larger than 21 can be knotted as well.

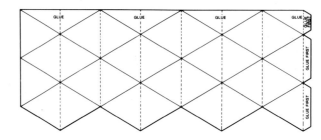

All angles are 30° 60° or 90°.

4

5

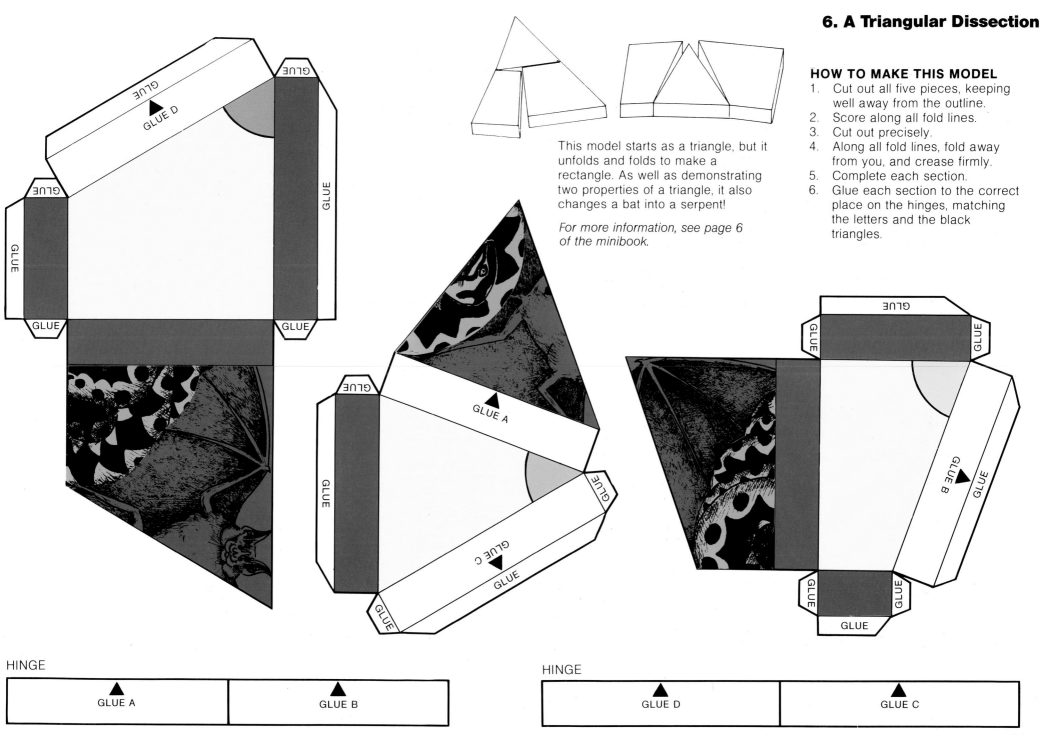

HOW TO MAKE THIS MODEL

1. Cut out all five pieces, keeping well away from the outline.
2. Score along all fold lines.
3. Cut out precisely.
4. Along all fold lines, fold away from you, and crease firmly.
5. Complete each section.
6. Glue each section to the correct place on the hinges, matching the letters and the black triangles.

This model starts as a triangle, but it unfolds and folds to make a rectangle. As well as demonstrating two properties of a triangle, it also changes a bat into a serpent!

For more information, see page 6 of the minibook.

GLUE
GLUE
GLUE D
GLUE
GLUE
GLUE
GLUE

GLUE
GLUE A
GLUE
GLUE C
GLUE

GLUE
GLUE
GLUE
GLUE B
GLUE
GLUE
GLUE

HINGE

GLUE A | GLUE B

HINGE

GLUE D | GLUE C

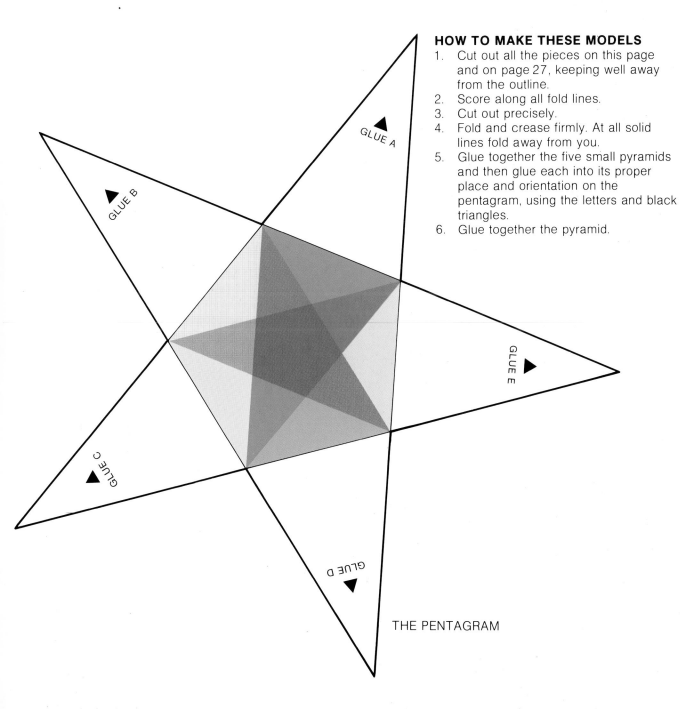

GLUE A

GLUE B

GLUE C

GLUE D

GLUE E

THE PENTAGRAM

HOW TO MAKE THESE MODELS

1. Cut out all the pieces on this page and on page 27, keeping well away from the outline.
2. Score along all fold lines.
3. Cut out precisely.
4. Fold and crease firmly. At all solid lines fold away from you.
5. Glue together the five small pyramids and then glue each into its proper place and orientation on the pentagram, using the letters and black triangles.
6. Glue together the pyramid.

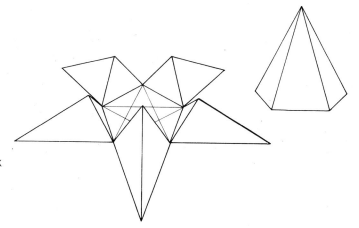

Two models, a pentagram and a pyramid give interesting colour arrangements as they fit together in various ways.

For more information, see page 7 of the minibook.

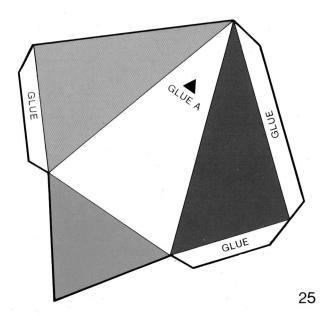

GLUE A

GLUE

GLUE

GLUE

To make these models, see page 25.

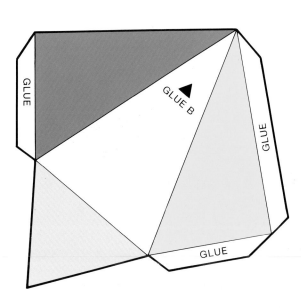

GLUE

GLUE B ▲

GLUE

GLUE

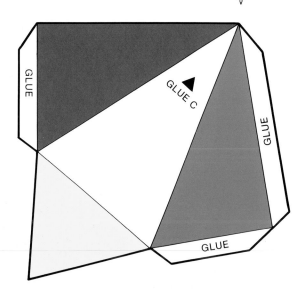

GLUE

GLUE C ▲

GLUE

GLUE

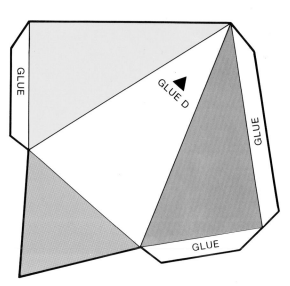

GLUE

GLUE D ▲

GLUE

GLUE

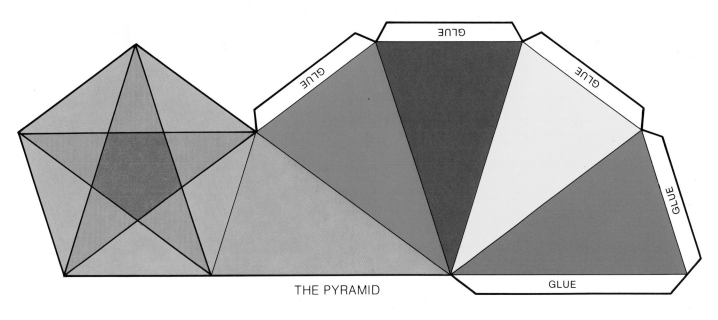

GLUE

GLUE

GLUE

GLUE

THE PYRAMID

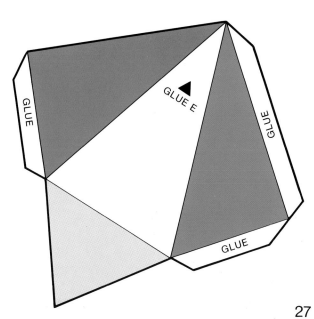

GLUE

GLUE E ▲

GLUE

GLUE

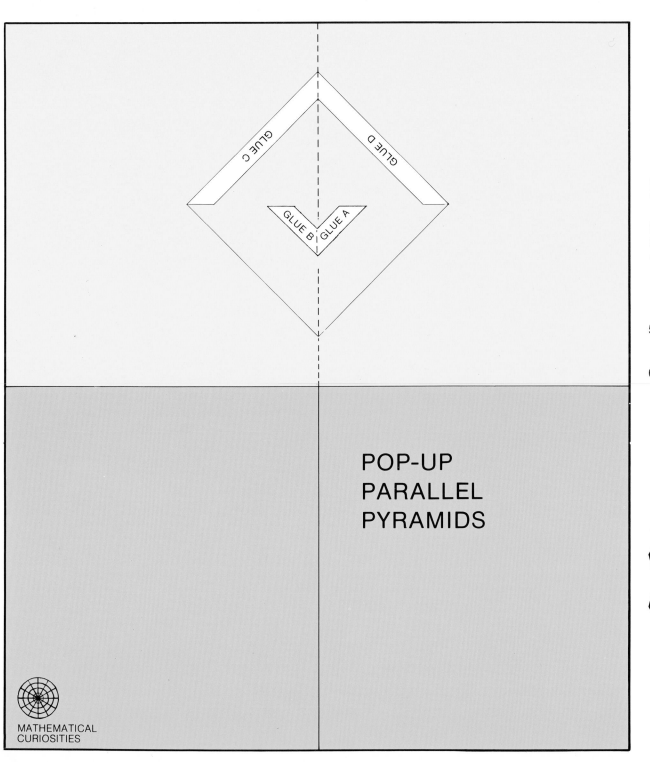

GLUE C
GLUE D
GLUE B | GLUE A

POP-UP
PARALLEL
PYRAMIDS

8. Pop-up Parallel Pyramids

As you open this 'book', a pyramid pops up — or rather two parallel pyramids pop-up, for there is a smaller one hidden inside!

For more information, see also page 8 of the minibook.

HOW TO MAKE THIS MODEL

1. Cut out all three pieces, keeping well away from the outline.
2. Score along all fold lines.
3. Cut out precisely.
4. Fold the 'book' in half away from you along the solid fold line and check that it matches. Spread glue smoothly inside the fold and press together. When dry, crease along the centre fold so that it closes with the dotted line inside.
5. To make each pyramid, fold away from you along each fold line and crease firmly. Then glue the flaps marked "GLUE*"
6. Glue the two pyramids in position on the 'book', smaller first. When you close it they will fold flat, ready to pop-up when it is opened again.

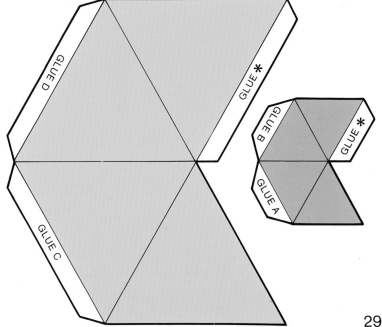

GLUE D
GLUE *
GLUE B
GLUE *
GLUE A
GLUE C